4-Chord Songbook
Bob Dylan

WISE PUBLICATIONS
part of The Music Sales Group
London / New York / Paris / Sydney / Copenhagen / Berlin / Madrid / Tokyo

This *4-Chord Songbook* allows even beginner guitarists to play and enjoy classic hits. With the same 4 chords used throughout the book, you'll soon master your favourite Bob Dylan songs.

The *4-Chord Songbook* doesn't use music notation. Throughout the book chord boxes are printed at the head of each song; the chord changes are shown above the lyrics. It's left to you, the guitarist, to decide on a strum pattern or picking pattern.

You might find that the pitch of the vocal line is not always comfortable because it is pitched too high or too low. In that case, you can change the key without learning a new set of chords; simply place a capo behind a suitable fret.

Whatever you do, this *4-Chord Songbook* guarantees hours of enjoyment for guitarists of all levels, as well as providing a fine basis for building a strong repertoire.

Published by
Wise Publications
14-15 Berners Street, London W1T 3LJ, UK.

Exclusive Distributors:
Music Sales Limited
Distribution Centre, Newmarket Road, Bury St Edmunds, Suffolk IP33 3YB, UK.
Music Sales Pty Limited
120 Rothschild Avenue, Rosebery, NSW 2018, Australia.

Order No. AM988185
ISBN 1-84609-820-3
This book © Copyright 2006 Wise Publications,
a division of Music Sales Limited.

Printed in the EU.

www.musicsales.com

Your Guarantee of Quality

As publishers, we strive to produce every book to the highest commercial standards.

The music has been freshly engraved and the book has been carefully designed to minimise awkward page turns and to make playing from it a real pleasure.

Particular care has been given to specifying acid-free, neutral-sized paper made from pulps which have not been elemental chlorine bleached.

This pulp is from farmed sustainable forests and was produced with special regard for the environment.

Throughout, the printing and binding have been planned to ensure a sturdy, attractive publication which should give years of enjoyment.

If your copy fails to meet our high standards, please inform us and we will gladly replace it.

All I Really Want To Do

Words & Music by Bob Dylan

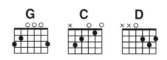

Intro | G | G ||

Verse 1

```
C   G         D    G
I ain't lookin' to compete with you,
C   G      D    G
Beat or cheat or mistreat you,
C   G      D    G
Simplify you, classify you,
   C   G    D   G
Deny, defy or crucify you.
G   D           G   C  G
All I really want to do ____
    D     G         C
Is, baby, be friends with you.
```

Link 1 | G   C | G   C | G   D |

| G   C | G | G ||

Verse 2

```
G        C   G      D       G
   No, and I ain't lookin' to fight with you,
C   G      D    G
Frighten you or uptighten you,
C   G      D       G
Drag you down or drain you down,
C   G      D       G
Chain you down or bring you down.
G   D           G   C  G
All I really want to do _____
    D     G         C
Is, baby, be friends with (you.)
```

Link 2 |G C |G C |G D |G C D |G C |G ||
                 you.

Verse 3
```
C     G       D       G
I ain't lookin' to block you up
C      G       D      G
Shock or knock or lock you up,
C  G       D      G
Analyze you, categorise you,
C  G         D   G
Finalise you or advertise you.
G  D              G   C  G
All I really want to do _____
     D      G          C
Is, baby, be friends with you.
```

Link 3 |G   D |G C |G   D |G C |G ||

Verse 4
```
C     G    D          G
I don't want to straight-face you,
C      G        D       G
Race or chase you, track or trace you,
C   G        D      G
Or disgrace you or displace you,
C  G       D   G
Or define you or confine you.
G  D              G   C  G
All I really want to do _____
     D      G          C
Is, baby, be friends with you.
```

Link 4 |G   D |G C |G   D |G C |G ||

Verse 5
```
C    G      D       G
I don't want to meet your kin,
C        G      D    G
Make you spin or do you in,
C   G       D   G
Or select you or dissect you,
C    G         D  G
  Or inspect you or reject you.
G  D              G   C  G
All I really want to do _____
     D      G          C
Is, baby, be friends with you.
```

Link 5

```
‖: G   D  | G   C   | G   D   | G   C   :‖
 | G   D  | G   C   | G   D   | G   C   | G   ‖
```

Verse 6

    C   G   D   G
I don't want to fake you out,

    C   G   D   G
Take or shake or forsake you out,

    C   G   D   G
I ain't looking for you to feel like me,

    C   G   D   G
See like me or be like me.

    G   D   G   C   G
All I really want to do _____

         D   G   C
Is, baby, be friends with you.

Link 6

```
‖: G   D  | G   C   | G   D   | G   C   :‖
```

                                            Repeat to fade

All Along The Watchtower

Words & Music by Bob Dylan

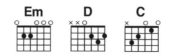

Intro

‖: Em D | C   D | Em D | C   D :‖

Verse 1

Em   D   C   D
    "There must be some way out of here,"
Em   D   C   D
    Said the joker to the thief,
Em   D   C   D
    "There's too much confusion,
Em   D   C   D
    I can't get no relief.
Em   D   C   D
    Businessmen, they drink my wine,
Em   D   C   D
    Plowmen   dig my earth,
Em   D   C   D
    None of them along the line
Em   D   C   D
    Know what any of it is worth."

Link

‖: Em D | C   D | Em D | C   D :‖

Verse 2

Em   D   C   D
    "No reason to get excited,"
Em   D   C   D
    The thief, he kindly spoke,
Em   D   C   D
    "There are many here among us
Em   D   C   D
    Who feel that life is but a joke.

cont.

Em   D   C   D
But you and I, we've been through that,

Em   D   C   D
And this is not our fate,

Em   D   C   D
So let us not talk falsely now,

Em   D   C   D
The hour is getting late."

Link

‖: Em D | C   D | Em D | C   D :‖

Verse 3

Em   D   C   D
All along the watchtower,

Em   D   C D
Princes kept the view

Em   D   C   D
While all the women came and went,

Em   D   C D
Barefoot servants, too.

Em   D   C   D
Outside in the distance

Em   D   C   D
A wildcat did growl,

Em   D   C   D
Two riders   were approaching,

Em   D   C D
The wind began to howl.

Coda

| Em D | C   D | Em D | C   D |

| Em D | C   D | Em   ‖

Blowin' In The Wind

Words & Music by Bob Dylan

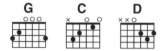

Intro | G ‖

Verse 1
G   C   D   G
How many roads must a man walk down
          C   G
Before you call him a man?
               C   D   G
Yes, 'n' how many seas must a white dove sail
          C   D
Before she sleeps in the sand?
         G   C   D   G
Yes, 'n' how many times must the cannon balls fly
         C   G
Before they're forever banned?

Chorus 1
        C   D   G   C
The answer, my friend, is blowin' in the wind,
          D   G
The answer is blowin' in the wind.

Link 1 | C D | G C | C D | G ‖

Verse 2

```
            G          C            D              G
Yes, 'n' how many years can a mountain exist
              C              G
Before it is washed to the sea?
                    C            D          G
Yes, 'n' how many years can some people exist
              C          D
Before they're allowed to be free?
            G      C        D          G
Yes, 'n' how many times can a man turn his head,
                  C              G
And pretend that he just doesn't see?
```

Chorus 2   As Chorus 1

Link 2 | C D | G C | C D | G   ‖

Verse 3

```
                  C            D          G
Yes 'n' how many times must a man look up
              C      G
Before he can see the sky?
                    C          D        G
Yes, 'n' how many ears must one man have
              C            D
Before he can hear people cry?
            G        C          D              G
Yes, 'n' how many deaths will it take till he knows
                  C                  G
That too many people have died?
```

Chorus 3   As Chorus 1

Coda | C D | G C | C D | G   ▌

Everything Is Broken

Words & Music by Bob Dylan

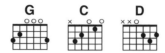

Verse 1

G
Broken lines, broken strings,

Broken threads, broken springs,
C
Broken idols, broken heads,
G
People sleeping in broken beds.
D
Ain't no use jiving,
C
Ain't no use joking,
G
Everything is broken.

Verse 2

G
Broken bottles, broken plates,

Broken switches, broken gates,
C
Broken dishes, broken parts,
G
Streets are filled with broken hearts.
D   **C**
Broken words never meant to be spoken,
G
Everything is broken.

Solo | **G** | **G** | **G** | **G** |

Bridge

    D
Seem like every time you stop and turn around,
    C
  Something else just hit the ground.

Verse 3

    G
  Broken cutters, broken saws,

Broken buckles, broken laws,
    C
Broken bodies, broken bones,
    G
Broken voices on broken phones.
    D   C
Take a deep breath, feel like you're chokin',
    G
Everything is broken.

Solo |G |G |G |G |

Bridge 2

    D
Every time you leave and go off someplace,
    C
  Things fall to pieces in my face.

Verse 4

    G
  Broken hands on broken ploughs,

Broken treaties, broken vows,
    C
  Broken pipes, broken tools,
    G
  People bending broken rules.
    D   C
  Hound dog howling, bull frog croaking,
    G
  Everything is broken.

Forever Young

Words & Music by Bob Dylan

G   C   D   Em

Intro
| G | G | G | G ||

Verse 1

G
May God bless and keep you always,
D
May your wishes all come true,
C
May you always do for others
    G
And let others do for you.

May you build a ladder to the stars
  D
And climb on every rung,
  C   **D**
May you stay
  G
Forever young,

Chorus 1

    D   **Em**
Forever young, _____ forever young, _____
   G   **D**   **G**
May you stay __ forever young.

Verse 2

  G
May you grow up to be righteous,
  D
May you grow up to be true,
  C
May you always know the truth
     G
And see the lights surrounding you.

cont.   May you always be courageous,

               D
          Stand upright and be strong,

                    C   **D**
          And may you stay

               G
          Forever young,

               D   **Em**
Chorus 2   Forever young, _____ forever young, _____

                   G   **D**   **G**
          May you stay _____ forever   young.

               G
Verse 3   May your hands always be busy,

               D
          May your feet always be swift,

               C
          May you have a strong foundation

                                     G
          When the winds of changes shift. ___

          May your heart always be joyful,

               D
          May your song always be sung,

               G   **D**
          May you stay

               G
          Forever   young,

               D   **Em**
Chorus 3   Forever young, _____ forever young, _____

                   G   **D**   **G**
          May you stay ___ forever young.

Coda

G	D	C	C	G	G	
G	D	C	D	G	G	
D	D	Em	Em			
G	D	G	G			

Highway 61 Revisited

Words & Music by Bob Dylan

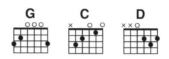

Intro | G | G | G | G |

Verse 1
          G
Oh God   said to Abraham, "Kill me a son"

Abe says, "Man, you must be puttin' me on"

God say, "No." Abe say, "What?"

God say, "You can do what you want Abe, but
   C   **G**
The next time you see me comin' you better run"
   D
Well Abe says, "Where do you want this killin' done?"
   G
God   says, "Out on Highway 61."

Verse 2
Well Georgia Sam he had a bloody nose

Welfare Department they wouldn't give him no clothes

He asked poor Howard where can I go

Howard said there's only one place I know
C   **G**
Sam said tell me quick man I got to run
   D
Ol' Howard just pointed with his gun
     G
And said that way down on Highway 61.

Verse 3   Well Mack the Finger said to Louie the King

I got forty red white and blue shoe strings

And a thousand telephones that don't ring

Do you know where I can get rid of these things

        C   G
And Louie the King said let me think for a minute son

              D
And he said yes I think it can be easily done

          G
Just take everything down to Highway 61.

Verse 4   Now the fifth daughter on the twelfth night

Told the first father that things weren't right

My complexion she said is much too white

                                                    C
He said come here and step into the light he says hmm you're right

                                  G
Let me tell the second mother this has been done

            D
But the   second mother was with the seventh son

          G
And they were both out on Highway 61.

Verse 5   Now the rovin' gambler he was very bored

He was tryin' to create a next world war

He found a promoter who nearly fell off the floor

He said I never engaged in this kind of thing before

        C   G
But   yes I think it can be very easily done.

               D
We'll just put   some bleachers out in the sun

          G
And have it on Highway 61.

A Hard Rain's A-Gonna Fall

Words & Music by Bob Dylan

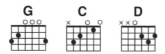

G   C   D

Intro | G C G | G ||

Verse 1

            G   C   G
Oh, where have you been, my blue-eyed son?

                                             D
Oh, where have you been, my darling young one?

     C   D   G
I've stumbled on the side of twelve misty mountains,

              C   D   G
I've walked   and I've crawled on six crooked highways,

             C   D   G
I've stepped   in the middle of seven sad forests,

     C   D   G
I've been out in front of a dozen dead oceans,

              C   D   G
I've been ten thousand miles in the mouth of a graveyard,

                                   D   G   C
And it's a hard, and it's a hard, it's a hard, and it's a hard,

     G   D   G   C G
It's a hard rain's _____ a-gonna fall.

Verse 2

            G   C   G
Oh, what did you see, my blue-eyed son?

                                      D
Oh, what did you see, my darling young one?

        C   D   G
I saw a newborn baby with wild wolves all around it

            C   D   G
I saw a highway of diamonds with nobody on it,

           C   D   G
I saw a black branch with blood that kept dripping,

cont.

        C   D   G
I saw a room full of men with their hammers a-bleeding,

     C   D   G
I saw a white ladder all covered with water,

        C   D   G
I saw ten thousand talkers whose tongues were all broken,

        C   D   G
I saw guns and sharp swords in the hands of young children,

               D   G   C
And it's a hard, it's a hard, it's a hard, and it's a hard,

     G   D   G   C   G
It's a hard rain's _____ a-gonna fall.

Verse 3

       G   C   G
And what did you hear, my blue-eyed son?

                                 D
And what did you hear, my darling young one?

        C   D   G
I Heard the sound of a thunder, it roared out a warnin',

        C   D   G
Heard the roar of a wave that could drown the whole world,

        C   D   G
Heard one hundred drummers whose hands were a-blazin',

        C   D   G
Heard ten thousand whisperin' and nobody listenin',

        C   D   G
Heard one person starve, I heard many people laughing,

         C   D   G
Heard the song of a poet who died in the gutter,

         C   D   G
Heard the sound of a clown who cried in the alley,

               D   G   C
And it's a hard, it's a hard, it's a hard, it's a hard,

     G   D   G   C   G
It's a hard rain's _____ a-gonna fall.

Verse 4

       G   C   G
Oh, who did you meet, my blue-eyed son?

                               D
Oh, who did you meet, my darling young one?

        C   D   G
I met a young child beside a dead pony,

        C   D   G
I met a white man who walked a black dog,

cont.

      C   D   G
I met a young woman whose body was burning,

      C   D   G
I met a young girl, she gave me a rainbow,

      C   D   G
I met one man who was wounded in love,

      C   D   G
I met another man who was wounded in hatred,

                    D   G   C
And it's a hard, it's a hard, it's a hard, it's a hard,

      G   D   G   C   G
It's a hard rain's _____ a-gonna fall.

Verse 5

      G   C   G   C   G
Oh, what'll you do now, my blue-eyed son?

                               D
Oh, what'll you do now, my darling young one?

      C   D   G
I'm a-goin' back out 'fore the rain starts a-falling,

      C   D   G
I'll walk to the depths of the deepest black forest,

        C   D   G
Where the people are many and their hands are all empty,

      C   D   G
Where the pellets of poison are flooding their waters,

        C   D   G
Where the home in the valley meets the damp dirty prison,

      C   D   G
And the executioner's face is always well hidden,

      C   D   G
Where hunger is ugly, where souls are forgotten,

      C   D   G
Where black is the color, where none is the number,

      C   D   G
And I'll tell it and think it and speak it and breathe it,

      C   D   G
And reflect it from the mountain so all souls can see it,

      C   D   G
Then I'll stand on the ocean until I start sinkin',

      C   D   G
But I'll know my song well before I start singin',

          D   G   C
And it's a hard, it's a hard, it's a hard, and it's a hard,

      G   D   G   C   G
It's a hard rain's _____ a-gonna fall.

18

Isis

Words by Bob Dylan & Jacques Levy
Music by Bob Dylan

G   **C**   **D**

Intro | D | D | D | D ||

Verse 1
D   C   G   D
I married Isis on the fifth day of May,
                C   G   D
But I could not hold on to her very long.
              C   G   D
So I cut off my hair and I rode straight away
                    C   G   D |D |D ||
For the wild unknown country where I could not go wrong.

Verse 2
D   C   G   D
I came to a high place of darkness and light.
              C   G   D
The dividing line ran through the centre of town.
             C   G   D
I hitched up my pony to a post on the right,
             C   G   D |D |D ||
Went into a laundry to wash my clothes down.

Verse 3
D   C   G   D
A man in the corner approached me for a match.
             C   G   D
I knew right away he was not ordinary.
             C   G   D
He said, "Are you lookin' for somethin' easy to catch?"
             C   G   D
I said, "I got no money." He said, "That ain't necessary."

Link 1 || D C | G D :||

Verse 4
D   C   G   D
We set out that night for the cold in the north.
            C   G   D
I gave him my blanket, he gave me his word.
             C   G   D
I said, "Where are we goin'?" He said we'd be back by the fourth,
             C   G D
I said, "That's the best news that I've ever heard."

Link 2 || D C | G D :||

Verse 5

| D | C | G | D |

I was thinkin' about turquoise, I was thinkin' about gold,

| | C | G | D |

I was thinkin' about diamonds and the world's biggest necklace.

| | C | G | D | | D | |

As we rode throught the canyons, through the devilish cold,

| | C | G | D |

I was thinkin' about Isis, how she thought I was so reckless.

Verse 6

| D | C | G | D |

How she told me that one day we would meet up again,

| | C | G | D |

And things would be different the next time we wed,

| | C | G | D |

If I could only hang on and just be her friend.

| | C | G | D |

I still can't remember all the best things she said.

Link 3

‖: D   C | G   D :‖

Verse 7

| D | C | G | D |

We came to the pyramids all embedded in ice.

| | C | G | D |

He said, "There's a body I'm tryin' to find,

| | C | G | D |

If I carry it out it'll bring a good price."

| | C | G | D |

'Twas then that I knew what he had on his mind.

Verse 8

| D | C | G |

The wind it was howlin' and the snow was outrageous.

| | C | G | D |

We chopped through the night and we chopped through the dawn.

| | C | G | D |

When he died I was hopin' that it wasn't contagious,

| | C | G | D |

But I made up my mind that I had to go on.

Link 4

‖: D   C | G   D :‖

Verse 9

| D | C   G | D |

I broke into the tomb, but the casket was empty.

| | C   G | D |

There was no jewels, no nothin', I felt I'd been had.

| | C   G | D |

When I saw that my partner was just bein' friendly,

| | C   G | D |

When I took up his offer I must-a been mad.

Link 5
‖: D C | G D :‖ *Play four times*

| D | D ‖

Verse 10

      D   C   G   D
I picked up his body and I dragged him inside,
                     C   G   D
Threw him down in the hole and I put back the cover.
                C   G D
I said a quick prayer and I felt satisfied.
                  C   G   D   D | D   ‖
Then I rode back to find Isis to tell her I love her.

Link 6
‖: D C G D :‖ *Play four times*

Verse 11

           D   C   G   D
She was there in the meadow where the creek used to rise.
              C   G   D
Blinded by sleep and in need of a bed,
               C   G   D
I came in from the East with the sun in my eyes.
               C   D
I cursed her one time then I rode on ahead.

Verse 12

          D   C   G   D
She said, "Where ya been?" I said, "No place special."
                    C   G   D
She said, "You look different." I said, "well, not quite."
                    C   G   D
She said, "You been gone." I said, "That's only natural."
                    C   G D
She said, "You gonna stay?" I said, "Yeah, I jes might."

Link 7
‖: D C | G D :‖ *Play four times*

Verse 13

      D   C   G   D
Isis, oh, Isis, you mystical child.
                   C   G   D
What drives me to you is what drives me insane.
            C   G   D
I still can remember the way that you smiled
               C   G   D
On the fifth day of May in the drizzlin' rain.

Outro
‖: D C | G D :‖ *Play four times*

Is Your Love In Vain?

Words & Music by Bob Dylan

G   C   D   Em

Intro ‖: G | D | Em | G | C | D | G | G :‖ **1.**

2.
| C | D | D ‖ Em | D | C | G | C |

| C | D | D | G | D | Em | G | C |

| D | G | G ‖

Verse 1

      G   D   Em   G
Do you love me,
        C   D
Or are you just extending goodwill?
      G   D   Em   G
Do you need me half as bad as you say,
        C   D
Or are you just feeling guilt?
         Em   D   C   G
I've been burned before and I know the score,
        C   D
So you won't hear me complain.
G   D   Em   G
Will I be able to count on you,
C   D   G
Or is your love in vain?

Verse 2

      G   D   Em   G
Are you so fast that you cannot see
        C   D   G
That I must have solitude?
         D   Em   G
When I am in the darkness,
C   D
Why do you intrude?
       Em   D   C   G
Do you know my world, do you know my kind
C   D
Or must I explain?
G   D   Em   D
Will you let me be myself,
      C   D   G
Or is your love in vain?

Link

```
         C            D              G              Em
Well I've been to the mountain and I've been in the wind,
         C        D      F
I've been in and out of happiness.
         C        D              G      Em
I have dined with kings, I've been offered wings,
         C            D
And I've never been too impressed.
```

Verse 3

```
G D      Em    G
Alright, I'll take a chance,
         C     D     G
I will fall in love with you.
         D         Em        G
If I'm a fool, you can have the night,
         C               D
You can have the morning too.
         Em       D        C    G
Can you cook and sew, make flowers grow,
         C               D
Do you understand my pain?
G        D        Em    G
  Are you willing to risk it all,
         C     D    G
Or is your love in vain?
```

Instrumental

```
| G  | D  | Em | G  | C  | D  | G  | G  |

| G  | D  | Em | G  | C  | C  | D  | D  ||
```

Verse 4

```
         Em       D        C    G
Can you cook and sew, make flowers grow,
         C               D
Do you understand my pain?
G        D        Em    G
  Are you willing to risk it all,
         C     D    G
Or is your love in vain?
```

Outro

```
| G  D | Em | G  | C  | D  | G  | G  ||
```

Just Like Tom Thumb's Blues

Words & Music by Bob Dylan

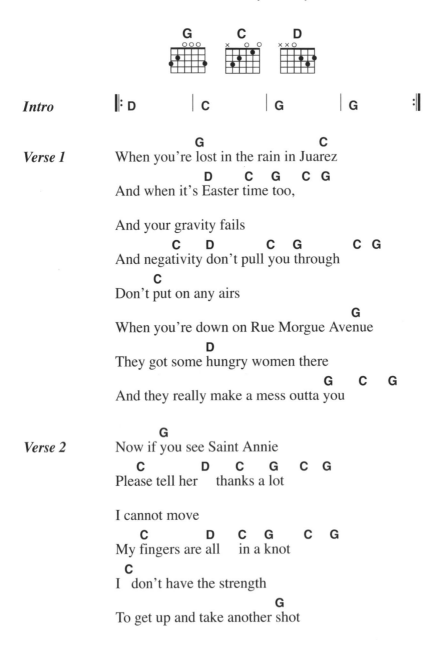

Intro ‖: D | C | G | G :‖

Verse 1
                      G   **C**
When you're lost in the rain in Juarez
                   D   **C** **G** **C G**
And when it's Easter time too,

And your gravity fails
               C   **D**   **C** **G**   **C G**
And negativity don't pull you through
               C
Don't put on any airs
                                               G
When you're down on Rue Morgue Avenue
                    D
They got some hungry women there
                                  G   **C**   **G**
And they really make a mess outta you

Verse 2
                      G
Now if you see Saint Annie
         C   **D** **C** **G** **C G**
Please tell her   thanks a lot

I cannot move
         C   **D** **C** **G**   **C G**
My fingers are all   in a knot
         C
I don't have the strength
                              G
To get up and take another shot

<pre>
              D
And my best friend, my doctor
                        G   C G
Won't even say what it is I've got

              G
Verse 3   Sweet Melinda
              C   G   C G
The peasants call her the goddess of   gloom

She speaks good English
                    C   D C G   C G
And she invites you up into her room
                    C
And you're so kind
                            G   C G
And careful not to go to her too soon
              D
And she takes your voice
                            G   C G
And leaves you howling at the moon

                    G
Verse 4   Up on Housing Project Hill
              C   G
                It's either fortune or fame

You must pick up one or the other
                    C   D   C   G   C G
Though neither of them are to be what they   claim
                    C
If you're lookin' to get silly
                            G   C G
You better go back to from where you came
                    D
Because the cops don't need you
                            G   C G
And man, they expect the same

                    G
Verse 5   Now all the authorities
              C   D   C G   C G
They just stand around   and boast
                                    C
How they blackmailed the sergeant-at-arms
                    D   C G   C G
Into leaving his post
</pre>

cont.

        C
And picking up Angel who

                  G   **C**   **G**
Just arrived here from the coast

          D
Who looked so fine at first

             G   **C**   **G**
But left looking just like a   ghost

Solo

‖: **G** | **C** **D** **C** | **G** **C** | **G**   :‖

| **C** | **C** | **G** **C** | **C** |

| **D** | **D** | **G** **C** | **G**   ‖

Verse 6

        G
I started out on burgundy

        C   **D**   **C** **G**   **C** **G**
But soon hit the hard - er   stuff

                           C
Everybody said they'd stand behind me

            D   **C** **G**   **C** **G**
When the game got rough

        C
But the joke was on me

                    G   **C** **G**
There was nobody even there to bluff

         D
I'm going back to New York City

              G   **C** **G**
I do believe I've had enough

Coda   ‖: **D** | **C** | **G** | **G**   :‖ *Repeat to fade*

Mississippi

Words & Music by Bob Dylan

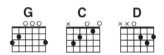

Intro | G | C D G ‖

Verse 1

G
Every step of the way

We walk the line

                                      C
Your days are numbered, so are mine
G   C
Time is pilin' up,
G   C
We struggle and we scrape.
G   C
We're all— boxed in,
D   C
Nowhere to es - cape

City's just a jungle, more games to play.
                                              C
Trapped in the heart of it, trying to get a - way
            G   C   G   C
I was raised in the country, I been workin' in the town
G   C   D   G
I been in trouble ever since I set my suitcase down.

Chorus 1

D   G
Got nothing for you, I had nothing before
D   C   D
Don't even have anything for my - self any - more
            D   G
Sky full of fire,— pain pourin' down
D   C   D
Nothing you can sell me, I'll see you a - round

Verse 2

G
All my powers of ex - pression and thoughts so sublime
                                                   C
Could never do you justice in reason or rhyme
G   C   G   C
Only one thing I did wrong
G   C   D   G
Stayed in Mississip - pi— a day too long

| G   C | D   G |

G
Well, the devil's in the alley, mule's in the stall
                                                C
Say anything you wanna, I have heard it all
G   C   G   C
I was thinking about the things that Rosie said
G   C   D   G
I was dreaming I was sleeping in— Rosie's bed
G
Walking through the leaves, falling from the trees
                                  C
Feeling like a stranger nobody sees
G   C   G   C
So many things that we never will un - do
G   C   D   G
I— know you're sorry, I'm— sorry too

Chorus 2

D   G
Some people will offer you their hand and some won't
D   C   D
Last night I knew you, to - night I don't
                                        G
I need somethin' strong to distract my mind
D   C   D
I'm gonna look at you 'til my eyes go blind

Verse 3

G
Well I got here following the southern star

                                    C
I crossed that river just to be where you are

G   **C** **G** **G**
Only one thing I did wrong

G   **C** **D**   **G**
Stayed in Mississip - pi——— a day too long

| **G**   **C** | **D** **G** |

G
Well my ship's been split to splinters and it's sinking fast

                               C
I'm drowning in the poison, got no future, got no past

G
But my heart is not weary, it's light and it's free

                         C   **D**   **G**
I've got nothin' but affection for all those who've sailed with me

Everybody movin' if they ain't already there

                       C
Everybody got to move some - where

G   **C**   **G**   **C**
Stick with me baby, stick with me any - how

G   **C**   **D**   **G**
Things should start to get interest - ing—— right about now

Chorus 3

D   **G**
My clothes are wet,—— tight on my skin

D   **C**   **D**
Not as tight as the corner that I painted myself in

                       G
I know that fortune is waiting to be kind

D   **C**   **D**
So give me your hand and say you'll be mine

Verse 4

G
Well, the emptiness is endless, cold as the clay

                                           C
You can always come back, but you can't come back all the way

G   **C** **G**   **C**
Only one thing I did wrong

G   **C** **D**   **G**
Stayed in Mississip - pi——— a day too long

Outro | **G**   **C** | **D**   **G**   ‖

Mr. Tambourine Man

Words & Music by Bob Dylan

G   C   D

Intro | G | G ||

Chorus 1
```
C        D                G          C
Hey! Mr. Tambourine Man, play a song for me,
      G              C           D
I'm not sleepy and there is no place I'm going to.
C        D                G          C
Hey! Mr. Tambourine Man, play a song for me,
      G              C           D        C
In the jingle jangle morning I'll come followin' you.
```

Verse 1
```
             C                  D        G           C
Though I know that evenin's empire has returned into sand,
G                    C
Vanished from my hand,
      G               C              D
Left me blindly here to stand but still not sleeping.
     C         D             G          C
My weariness amazes me, I'm branded on my feet,
      G              C
I have no one to meet,
      G               C                 D
And the ancient empty street's too dead for dreaming.
```

Chorus 2   As Chorus 1

Link 1 | G | G ||

Verse 2
```
     C         D                G          C
Take me on a trip upon your magic swirlin' ship,
      G              C          G              C
My senses have been stripped, my hands can't feel to grip,
      G             C          G
My toes too numb to step, wait only for my boot heels
      D
To be wanderin'.
     C         D              G          C
I'm ready to go anywhere, I'm ready for to fade
      G              C          G              C
Into my own parade, cast your dancing spell my way,
                      D
I promise to go under it.
```

| *Chorus 3* | As Chorus 1 |

| *Link 2* | ‖ G ‖ G ‖ |

Verse 3

                            C   D
Though you might hear laughin', spinnin',

                  G   C
Swingin' madly across the sun,

                G   C   G   C
It's not aimed at anyone, it's just escapin' on the run

                G   C   D
And but for the sky there are no fences facin'.

              C   D   G   D
And if you hear vague traces of skippin' reels of rhyme

                G   C   G   C
To your tambourine in time, it's just a ragged clown behind,

                G   C   G
I wouldn't pay it any mind, it's just a shadow you're

                              D
Seein' that he's chasing.

| *Chorus 4* | As Chorus 3 |

Harmonica Break

‖ C D ‖ G D ‖ G C ‖ G C ‖ G C ‖

‖ G C ‖ G ‖ D ‖ C D ‖ G C ‖

‖ G C ‖ G C ‖ G ‖ D G ‖ C ‖

Verse 4

                    C   D   G   D
Then take me disappearin' through the smoke rings of my mind,

                G   C   G   C
Down the foggy ruins of time, far past the frozen leaves,

                G   C   G   C
The haunted, frightened trees, out to the windy beach,

                G   C   D
Far from the twisted reach of crazy sorrow.

                  C   D   G
Yes, to dance beneath the diamond sky with one hand waving free,

                G   C   G   C
Silhouetted by the sea, circled by the circus sands,

                G   C   G   C
With all memory and fate driven deep beneath the waves,

                G   D
Let me forget about today until tomorrow.

| *Chorus 5* | As Chorus 3 |
| | *Fade* |

| *Coda* | ‖ C D ‖ G C ‖ G C ‖ G C ‖ G C ‖ |

Not Dark Yet

Words & Music by Bob Dylan

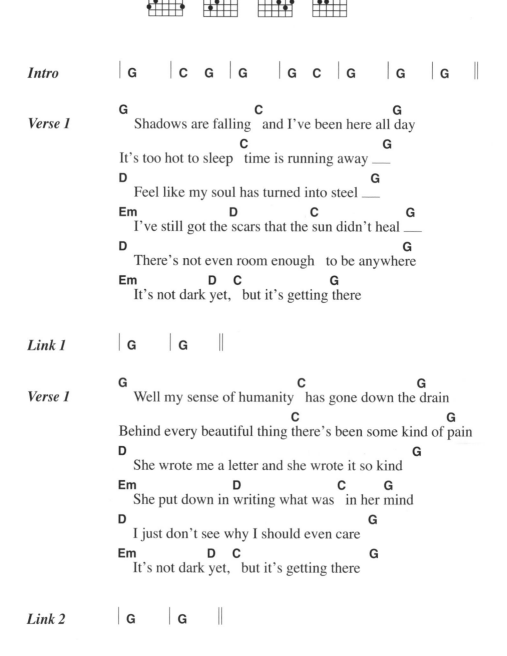

Intro | G | C G | G | G C | G | G | G ||

Verse 1
```
     G                          C                    G
      Shadows are falling    and I've been here all day
                          C                    G
It's too hot to sleep   time is running away __
D                                            G
    Feel like my soul has turned into steel __
Em                D            C              G
    I've still got the scars that the sun didn't heal __
D                                            G
    There's not even room enough   to be anywhere
Em                D  C              G
    It's not dark yet,   but it's getting there
```

Link 1 | G | G ||

Verse 1
```
     G                             C                G
      Well my sense of humanity   has gone down the drain
                                C                        G
Behind every beautiful thing there's been some kind of pain
D                                            G
    She wrote me a letter and she wrote it so kind
Em                D            C    G
    She put down in writing what was   in her mind
D                                        G
    I just don't see why I should even care
Em                D  C                    G
    It's not dark yet,   but it's getting there
```

Link 2 | G | G ||

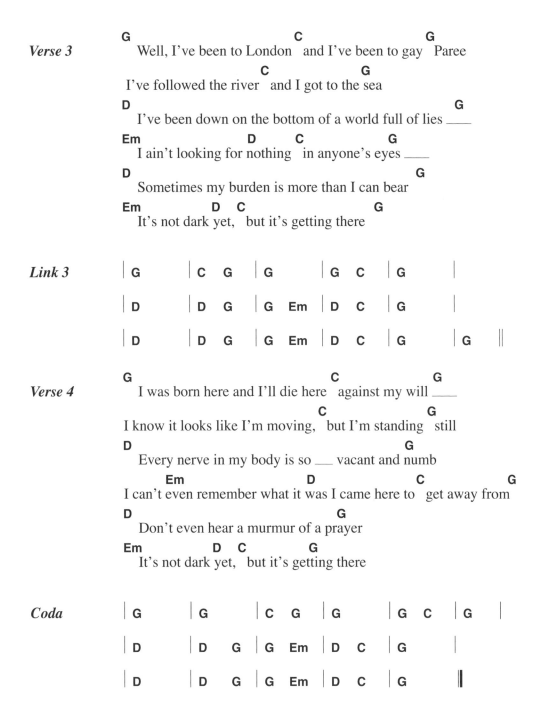

Verse 3

G   C   G
   Well, I've been to London and I've been to gay Paree
                             C   G
I've followed the river and I got to the sea
D   G
   I've been down on the bottom of a world full of lies ____
Em   D   C   G
   I ain't looking for nothing in anyone's eyes ____
D   G
   Sometimes my burden is more than I can bear
Em   D   C   G
   It's not dark yet, but it's getting there

Link 3

| G | C G | G | G C | G | |
| D | D G | G Em | D C | G | |
| D | D G | G Em | D C | G | G | ‖

Verse 4

G   C   G
   I was born here and I'll die here against my will ____
                              C   G
I know it looks like I'm moving, but I'm standing still
D   G
   Every nerve in my body is so __ vacant and numb
        Em   D   C   G
I can't even remember what it was I came here to get away from
D   G
   Don't even hear a murmur of a prayer
Em   D   C   G
   It's not dark yet, but it's getting there

Coda

| G | G | C G | G | G C | G | |
| D | D G | G Em | D C | G | | |
| D | D G | G Em | D C | G | | ‖

Quinn The Eskimo (The Mighty Quinn)

Words & Music by Bob Dylan

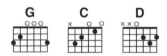

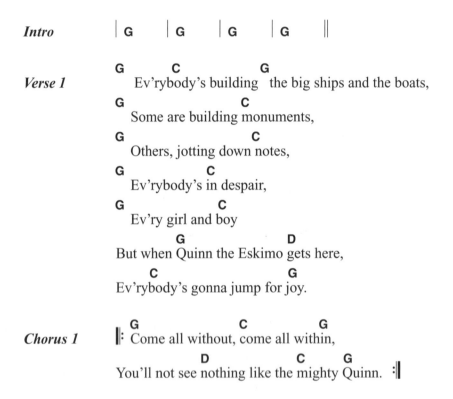

Intro | G | G | G | G ||

Verse 1

G   C   G
Ev'rybody's building   the big ships and the boats,

G   C
Some are building monuments,

G   C
Others, jotting down notes,

G   C
Ev'rybody's in despair,

G   C
Ev'ry girl and boy

              G   D
But when Quinn the Eskimo gets here,

        C   G
Ev'rybody's gonna jump for joy.

Chorus 1

   G   C   G
‖: Come all without, come all within,

               D   C   G
You'll not see nothing like the mighty Quinn. :‖

Verse 2

      G   **C**
I like to do just like the rest,

      G   **C**
I like my sugar sweet,

    G   **C**
  But guarding fumes and making haste,

     G   **C**
It ain't my cup of meat.

    G   **C**
  Ev'rybody's 'neath the trees,

    G   **C**
Feeding pigeons on a limb

          G   **D**
But when Quinn the Eskimo gets here,

     C   **G**
All the pigeons gonna run to him.

Chorus 2

     G   **C**   **G**
‖: Come all without, come all within,

             D   **C** **G**
You'll not see nothing like the mighty Quinn. :‖

Solo

| G C | G C | G C | G C | |

| G C | G C | G D | C G | ‖

Verse 3

  G   **C**
  A cat's meow and a cow's moo,

    G   **C**
I can recite 'em all,

   G   **C**
Tell me where it hurts you, honey,

    G   **C**
I'll tell you who to call.

   G   **C**
  Nobody can get no sleep,

           G   **C**
There's someone on ev'ryone's toes

         G   **D**
But when Quinn the Eskimo gets here,

    C   **G**
Ev'rybody's gonna wanna doze.

Chorus 3

     G   **C**   **G**
‖: Come all without, come all within,

             D   **C** **G**
You'll not see nothing like the mighty Quinn. :‖

Coda | G D | C G | ‖

Rainy Day Women #12 & 35

Words & Music by Bob Dylan

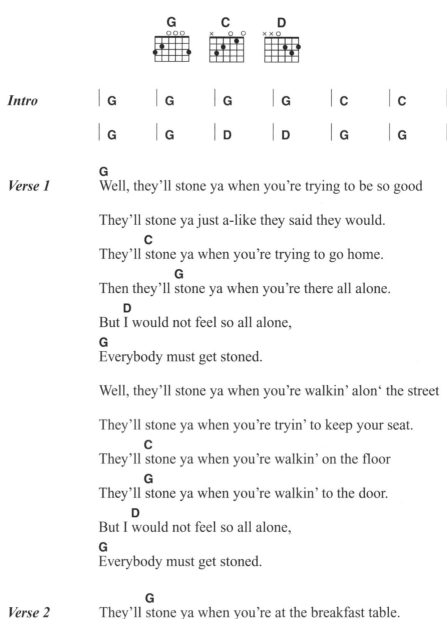

Intro

| G | | G | | G | | G | | C | | C | |
| G | | G | | D | | D | | G | | G | |

Verse 1

G
Well, they'll stone ya when you're trying to be so good

They'll stone ya just a-like they said they would.
    C
They'll stone ya when you're trying to go home.
       G
Then they'll stone ya when you're there all alone.
   D
But I would not feel so all alone,
G
Everybody must get stoned.

Well, they'll stone ya when you're walkin' alon' the street

They'll stone ya when you're tryin' to keep your seat.
    C
They'll stone ya when you're walkin' on the floor
    G
They'll stone ya when you're walkin' to the door.
   D
But I would not feel so all alone,
G
Everybody must get stoned.

Verse 2

     G
They'll stone ya when you're at the breakfast table.

They'll stone ya when you are young and able.
    C
They'll stone ya when you're trying to make a buck.

cont.

G
They'll stone ya and then they'll say, "good luck."

D
Tell ya what, I would not feel so all alone,

G
Everybody must get stoned.

Instrumental 1 | **G** | **G** | **G** | **G** | **C** | **C** |
| **G** | **G** | **D** | **D** | **G** | **G** ‖

G
Verse 3　Well, they'll stone you and say that it's the end.

Then they'll stone you and then they'll come back again.

C
They'll stone you when you're riding in your car.

G
They'll stone you when you're playing your guitar.

D
Yes, but I would not feel so all alone,

Everybody must get stoned.

Instrumental 2 | **G** | **G** | **G** | **G** | **C** | **C** |
| **G** | **G** | **D** | **D** | **G** | **G** ‖

G
Verse 4　Well, they'll stone you when you walk all alone.

They'll stone you when you are walking home.

C
They'll stone you and then say you are brave

G
They'll stone you when you are set down in your grave.

D
But I would not feel so all alone,

G
Everybody must get stoned.

Outro　　　| **G** | **G** | **G** | **G** |
| **C** | **C** | **G** | **G** ‖ *Fade out*

Shelter From The Storm

Words & Music by Bob Dylan

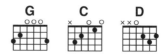

Intro | G | D | C | G |

Verse 1

```
G                       D        C                    D
'Twas in another life - time, one of toil and blood,
                            D              C
When blackness was a vir - tue and the road was full of mud.
G                      C          D
I came in from the wil - derness, a creature void of form,
            G
"Come in," she said,
             C                 G       | D  | C  | G      |
"I'll give you shelter from the storm."
```

Verse 2

```
(G)               D          C                       D
And if I pass this way again, you can rest assured,
                      D            C
I'll always do my best   for her, on that I give my word
            G                  C                        D
In a world of steel-eyed death, and men who are fighting to be warm.
            G
"Come in," she said,
             C                 G       | D  | C  | G      |
"I'll give you shelter from the storm."
```

Verse 3

```
(G)                              D   C                        D
Not a word was spoke between  us, there was little risk involved,
              D                     C
Everything up to   that point had been left unresolved.
G                 C          D
Try imagining a place   where it's always safe and warm.
         G
"Come in, " she said,
              C              G        | D    | C    | G        |
"I'll give you shelter from the storm. "
```

Verse 4

```
(G)                     D          C              D
I was burned out from ex - haustion, buried in the hail,
              D        C
Poisoned in the bush - es an' blown out on the trail,
G           C        D
Hunted like a crocodile, ravaged in the corn.
         G
"Come in," she said,
              C              G        | D    | C    | G        |
"I'll give you shelter from the storm."
```

Verse 5

```
(G)                      D  C                        D
Suddenly I turned around      and she was standin' there,
                    D           C
With silver bracelets on   her wrists and flowers in her hair.
G                        C         D
She walked up to me so grace - fully and took my crown of thorns.
         G
"Come in," she said,
              C              G        | D    | C    | G        |
"I'll give you shelter from the storm."
```

39

Verse 6

    (G)   D   C   D
Now there's a wall be - tween us, somethin' there's been lost,
                         D   C
I took too much for grant - ed, got my signals crossed.
G   C   D
Just to think that it all began on a long-forgotten morn.
      G
"Come in," she said,
             C   G | D | C | G |
"I'll give you shelter from the storm."

Verse 7

    (G)   D   C   D
Well, the deputy walks on hard nails and the preacher rides a mount,
                  D   C
But nothing really matters much, it's doom alone that counts
G   C   D
And the one-eyed undertak - er, he blows a futile horn.
      G
"Come in," she said,
             C   G | D | C | G |
"I'll give you shelter from the storm."

Verse 8

    (G)   D   C   D
I've heard newborn babies wailin' like a mournin' dove,
                  D   C
And old men with bro - ken teeth stranded without love.
      G   C   D
Do I understand your question, man, is it hopeless and forlorn?
      G
"Come in," she said,
             C   G | D | C | G |
"I'll give you shelter from the storm."

Verse 9

(G)   D   C   D
In a little hilltop vil - lage, they gambled for my clothes,

                         D   C
I bargained for salva - tion an' they gave me a lethal dose.

G   C   D
I offered up my in - nocence and got repaid with scorn.

                    G
"Come in," she said,

            C   G | D | C | G |
"I'll give you shelter from the storm."

Verse 10

(G)   D   C   D
Well, I'm livin' in a foreign country but I'm bound to cross the line,

                         D   C
Beauty walks a ra - zor's edge, someday I'll make it mine.

G   C   D
If I could only turn back the clock to when God and her were born.

                    G
"Come in," she said,

            C   G | D | C | G   ‖
"I'll give you shelter from the storm."

Subterranean Homesick Blues

Words & Music by Bob Dylan

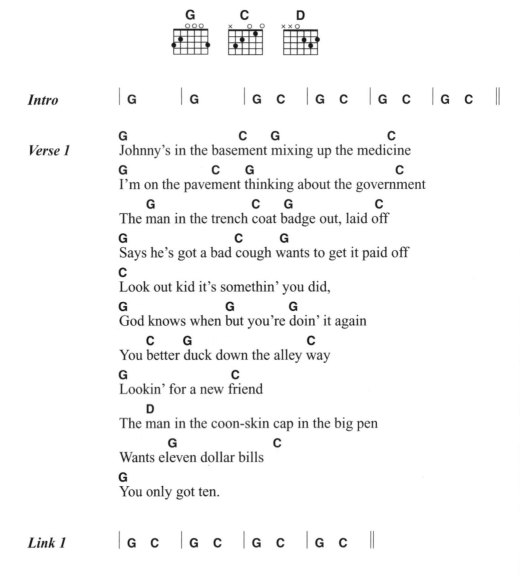

Intro | G | G | G C | G C | G C | G C ‖

Verse 1

G   C   G   C
Johnny's in the basement mixing up the medicine
G   C   G   C
I'm on the pavement thinking about the government
       G   C   G   C
The man in the trench coat badge out, laid off
G   C   G
Says he's got a bad cough wants to get it paid off
C
Look out kid it's somethin' you did,
G   G   G
God knows when but you're doin' it again
    C   G   C
You better duck down the alley way
G   C
Lookin' for a new friend
     D
The man in the coon-skin cap in the big pen
       G   C
Wants eleven dollar bills
G
You only got ten.

Link 1 | G C | G C | G C | G C ‖

```
                      G                 C  G                  C
Verse 2               Maggie comes fleetfoot, face full of black soot
                      G                 C  G              C
                      Talkin' that the heat put plants in the bed but
                          G                C  G                      C
                      The phone's tapped anyway, Maggie says that many say
                          G                C  G
                      They must bust in early May, orders from the D. A.
                      C
                      Look out kid don't matter what you did
                      G             C  G         C
                      Walk on your tip toes, don't try "No Doz",
                      G                      C           G
                      Better stay away from those that carry around a fire hose
                      D
                          Keep a clean nose, watch the plain clothes
                          G                    C
                      You don't need a weather man
                          G
                      To know which way the wind blows
```

Link 2 | G   C | G   C | G   C | G   C ||

```
                      G          C  G                C
Verse 3               Get sick, get well hang around a ink well
                      G              C  G                     C
                      Ring bell hard to tell if anything is goin' to sell
                      G          C    G            C
                      Try hard, get barred, get back, write braille
                      G             C  G
                      Get jailed, jump bail, join the army if you fail
                      C
                      Look out kid you're gonna get hit
                          G         C  G       C
                      But users, cheaters, six-time losers
                      G                   C
                      Hang around the theaters.
                      D
                      Girl by the whirlpool looking for a new fool
                      G              C
                      Don't follow leaders
                      G
                      Watch the parkin' meters
```

Link 3 | G   C | G   C | G   C | G   C ||

Verse 4

```
          G              C
Ah get born, keep warm
G              C      G
Short pants, romance, learn to dance
       C      G              C   G
Get dressed, get blessed, try to be a success
         C   G              C
Please her, please him, buy gifts
G
Don't steal, don't lift
```

Twenty years of schoolin'
```
C          G
And they put you on the day shift
C
Look out kid they keep it all hid
       G              C   G              C
Better jump down a manhole, light yourself a candle
G          C   G
Don't wear sandals, try to avoid the scandals
D
   Don't wanna be a bum, you better chew gum
       G              C
The pump don't work
           D
'Cause the vandals took the handles
```

Coda   ‖: D G | D G :‖ *Repeat to fade*

The Times They Are A-Changin'

Words & Music by Bob Dylan

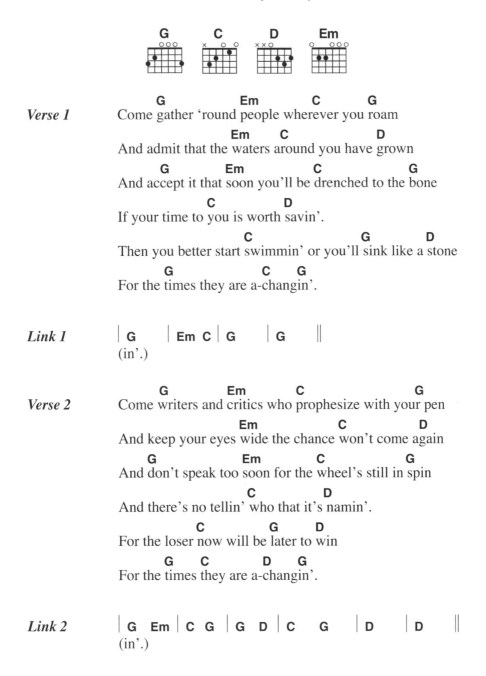

Verse 1

G   Em   C   G
Come gather 'round people wherever you roam
                   Em   C   D
And admit that the waters around you have grown
       G   Em   C   G
And accept it that soon you'll be drenched to the bone
             C   D
If your time to you is worth savin'.
                 C   G   D
Then you better start swimmin' or you'll sink like a stone
       G   C G
For the times they are a-changin'.

Link 1

| G | Em C | G | G ||
(in'.)

Verse 2

       G   Em   C   G
Come writers and critics who prophesize with your pen
                   Em   C   D
And keep your eyes wide the chance won't come again
       G   Em   C   G
And don't speak too soon for the wheel's still in spin
             C   D
And there's no tellin' who that it's namin'.
             C   G   D
For the loser now will be later to win
       G   C   D   G
For the times they are a-changin'.

Link 2

| G Em | C G | G D | C   G | D | D ||
(in'.)

Verse 3
```
        G           Em              C              G
Come senators, congressmen,  please heed the call
                    Em           C          D
Don't stand in the doorway, don't block up the hall
        G           Em        C          G
For he that gets hurt will be he who has stalled
                  C       D
There's a battle outside and it is ragin'.
                          C         G         D
Will soon shake your windows and rattle your walls
            G    C       D    G
For the times they are a-changin'.
```

Link 3 | G | D C | D G ‖
            (in')

Verse 4
```
        G           Em              C    G
Come mothers and fathers throughout the land
                Em            C          D
And don't criticize what you can't understand
        G           Em              C              G
Your sons and your daughters are beyond your command
                  C      D
Your old road is rapidly agin'.
                          C           G              D
Please get out of the new one if you can't lend your hand
            G              D    G
For the times they are a-changin'.
```

Link 4 | G | Em C | G | D   C |
            (in'.)

            | G   D | D   G | C   D | G | G   ‖

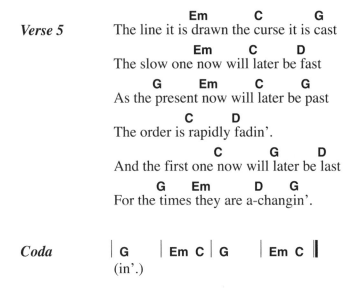

Verse 5

               Em   C   G
The line it is drawn the curse it is cast
                  Em   C   D
The slow one now will later be fast
          G   Em   C   G
As the present now will later be past
             C   D
The order is rapidly fadin'.
                 C   G   D
And the first one now will later be last
          G   Em   D   G
For the times they are a-changin'.

Coda | G | Em C | G | Em C ‖
           (in'.)

Relative Tuning

The guitar can be tuned with the aid of pitch pipes or dedicated electronic guitar tuners which are available through your local music dealer. If you do not have a tuning device, you can use relative tuning. Estimate the pitch of the 6th string as near as possible to E or at least a comfortable pitch (not too high, as you might break other strings in tuning up). Then, while checking the various positions on the diagram, place a finger from your left hand on the:

5th fret of the E or 6th string and **tune the open A** (or 5th string) to the note (A)

5th fret of the A or 5th string and **tune the open D** (or 4th string) to the note (D)

5th fret of the D or 4th string and **tune the open G** (or 3rd string) to the note (G)

4th fret of the G or 3rd string and **tune the open B** (or 2nd string) to the note (B)

5th fret of the B or 2nd string and **tune the open E** (or 1st string) to the note (E)

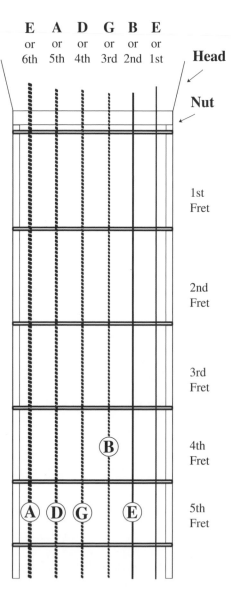

Reading Chord Boxes

Chord boxes are diagrams of the guitar neck viewed head upwards, face on as illustrated. The top horizontal line is the nut, unless a higher fret number is indicated, the others are the frets.

The vertical lines are the strings, starting from E (or 6th) on the left to E (or 1st) on the right.

The black dots indicate where to place your fingers.

Strings marked with an O are played open, not fretted. Strings marked with an X should not be played.

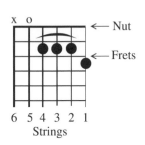

01/13(186137)